Little Fish Books about You and Me

C000132124

British Commonwealth Edition
Published by Scripture Union, England.

North American Edition Including Canada
Published by Regal Books
A Division of Gospel Light
Ventura, California, USA

© Gordon Stowell 1984

First Edition 1984
This reprint 2009

Co-edition arranged with the help of
Angus Hudson, London

Printed and Bound in Great Britain

Little Fish Books about You and Me

It's fun

illustrated by Gordon Stowell

It's fun to wake up each day

and to see the sun shining.

It's fun to play with my toys.

I can share them with others.

It's fun to run in the park,

and it's fun to feed the ducks.

It's fun
to see the animals and birds.

It's fun to look after my pets.

It's especially fun
on my birthday.

Thank You God very much.

It's fun to have good friends.

It's fun to play.
Thank You God.

It's fun to look at my books.

It's fun to listen to stories.

It's fun to splash in the bath,

and to feel the warm
cuddly towel.

It's fun
to jump into my cosy bed.

Thank You God.

It's fun

Little Fish Books about You and Me

Please God

Little Fish Books about You and Me

God knows

Little Fish Books about You and Me

Thank You God

Little Fish Books about You and Me

 Little Fish Books

I'm Sorry

Little Fish Books about You and Me

God loves

Little Fish Books about You and Me

Help me God

Little Fish Books about You and Me

I Like

Little Fish Books about You and Me

about You and Me